Macmillan
Science

Workbook

5

David and Penny Glover

MACMILLAN

C000184927

Contents

Lesson 1

Food and nutrition

1. Label these foods as coming from plants (P) or animals (A).

2. Unscramble the letters to make the names of five nutrients.

(If you are stuck look at this topic in your Pupil's Book for possible words.)

slneamri

bcaohyrdtraes

afst

_____   _____   _____

optiners

tavimnis

_____   _____

3. Write the name of the nutrient for each of these descriptions.

a They provide energy. Digestion breaks them into simple sugars: _____

b Needed for growth and repair. _____

c They supply energy and are used to build some body parts; excess is unhealthy.
  _____

d Special substances the body needs in small amounts but cannot make itself.
  _____

e Simple substances the body needs to build bones and perform other tasks.
  _____

4 **Living things:** Human body

4. **Explain briefly the importance of each of these minerals in the diet.**

a iron

_____

b calcium

_____

c salt

_____

Use the library and the Internet to learn more about the different minerals the body needs, and the foods that provide them.

Choose a mineral and write a brief report on it to present to the class.

_____

_____

_____

_____

_____

5. **Circle the word that matches the description.**

a These living things obtain nutrition from sunlight, air, water and soil.

plants / animals / bacteria

b These living things obtain nutrition by eating other living things.

plants / animals / bacteria

c This process breaks the food we eat into simpler substances that the body can use.

digestion / respiration / excretion

d This substance does not provide nutrition, but helps waste pass through the digestive system.

protein / fat / fibre

Food groups

1. **Write the name of the main nutrient in each of these foods.**

   a

   b

   c

   _____   _____   _____

2. **Mark each of these statements as true (✔) or false (✗).**

   a Rice is a good source of protein. ☐

   b Milk contains carbohydrate, protein, fat, minerals and vitamins. ☐

   c Humans are adapted to survive by eating only one type of food. ☐

   d Foods that contain fat turn an iodine solution black. ☐

3. **Look at the results of these food tests on foods A, B and C. Answer the questions.**

   a Which food (or foods) contains starch? _____

   b Which food (or foods) contains fat? _____

   iodine
   solution

   distilled
   water

   A   B   C

   food rubbed on
   filter paper

   paper washed

   A

   B

   C

4. **What foods have you eaten in the past 24 hours? What nutrients do these foods contain? Write the name of the food you have eaten for each of the food types listed below.**

   a A food from a plant. _____

   b A food from an animal. _____

   c A protein-rich food. _____

   d A carbohydrate-rich food. _____

   e A fatty food. _____

   f A mineral-rich food. _____

   g A vitamin-rich food. _____

   h A food that contains fibre. _____

A balanced diet

1. **Unscramble the words to make sentences that describe a balanced diet.**

healthy. to We mixture stay must eat a of foods different

_____

contains A diet balanced carbohydrates, proteins, vitamins, minerals and some fat.

_____

2. **Label the diagram. Label foods in this meal with the nutrients they provide. The chicken, for example, provides protein and some fat.**

protein and some fat

3. **List _four_ important uses of water in the body.**

a _____

b _____

c _____

d _____

4. The tables below give the water intake and water losses for two people during a day. Answer the questions.

Person A

Water intake in cm³	Water losses in cm³	
2800	urine	1500
	sweat	1000
	breathing out	400
	faeces	150

Person B

Water intake in cm³	Water losses in cm³	
2400	urine	1400
	sweat	550
	breathing out	370
	faeces	80

a Which person may be dehydrated? _____

b Which person's water is in balance? _____

c Explain how you know.

_____

_____

Food and energy

Activities 1, 2 and 3 refer to the experiment below.

Class five compared the energy content of different foods.

They used a candle to set fire to a 2 g sample of each food.

They used the burning food to heat 200 ml of water in a tin can.

They measured the initial temperature of the water and its final temperature when the sample had stopped burning.

These are their results.

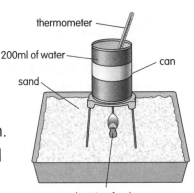

thermometer

200ml of water

sand

can

burning food

Food	Initial water temperature (°C)	Final water temperature (°C)	Temperature rise (°C)
dry bread	22	40	
nut	25	63	
chocolate	24	78	

1. **Complete the table by calculating the rise in water temperature each sample produced.**

2. **Answer the questions.**

   a Which food sample contained the greatest amount of energy per gram? _____

   b Which food sample contained the least amount of energy per gram? _____

   c Explain how you know.

   _____

   _____

3. **Explain briefly why the class took care to use the same mass of food and the same volume of water for each test.**

   _____

   _____

4. **Look at these food labels. Explain why it is better to snack on bread or dates than on chocolate.**

   Pitta bread
   Energy per 100 g
   275 calories

   Dates
   Energy per 100 g
   280 calories

   Chocolate
   Energy per 100 g
   504 calories

   _____

   _____

Digestion

1. **Label the parts of the alimentary canal.**

   > stomach   gullet   small intestine
   > anus   rectum   large intestine

   a _____

   b _____

   c _____

   d _____

   e _____

   f _____

2. **Mark each of these statements as true (✔) or false (✗).**

   a The alimentary canal is about 7 m long. ☐

   b You cannot swallow food when you are upside down. ☐

   c Digested food is absorbed in the stomach. ☐

   d Bacteria help to digest food in your intestines. ☐

3. **You swallow a ball of food. Label this diagram to explain how the food is moved through your gullet.**

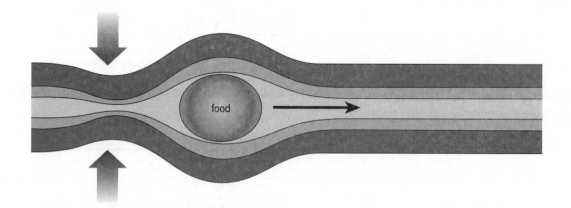

food

4. **You eat some bread and some dates. Describe briefly what happens to this food after you put it into your mouth.**

   _____

   _____

Producers and consumers

1. Unscramble the letters to make reasons why all living things require food. (If you are stuck look at this topic in your Pupil's Book for possible words.)

    To supply r n e e y g. _____

    To provide materials for w g r o h t. _____

    To supply materials for a e h l h t. _____

    To supply materials for p e a r i r s. _____

2. Explain in *two* sentences why plants are producers and animals are consumers.

    a Plants are producers because _____.

    b Animals are consumers because _____.

3. Photosynthesis is a chemical reaction that allows plants to capture and store the energy of sunlight. The reaction requires sunlight and two chemicals (reactants). The products of the reaction are two different chemicals.

    Write the reactants and products in the correct places on this flow chart.

    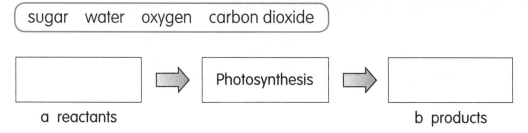

    sugar   water   oxygen   carbon dioxide

    [ ] ⟹ Photosynthesis ⟹ [ ]

    a reactants   b products

4. **Answer the questions.**

    a Name the gas labelled X. _____

    b Suggest how you could speed up the rate at which the plant makes gas bubbles.

    _____

    _____

    _____

    c How could you slow down the bubble rate?

    _____

    _____

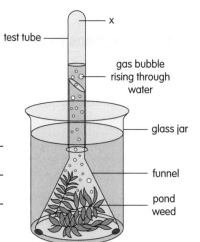

x

test tube

gas bubble rising through water

glass jar

funnel

pond weed

Energy flow in a food chain

1. **The arrows in this energy diagram show how energy flows in a food chain. Answer the questions.**

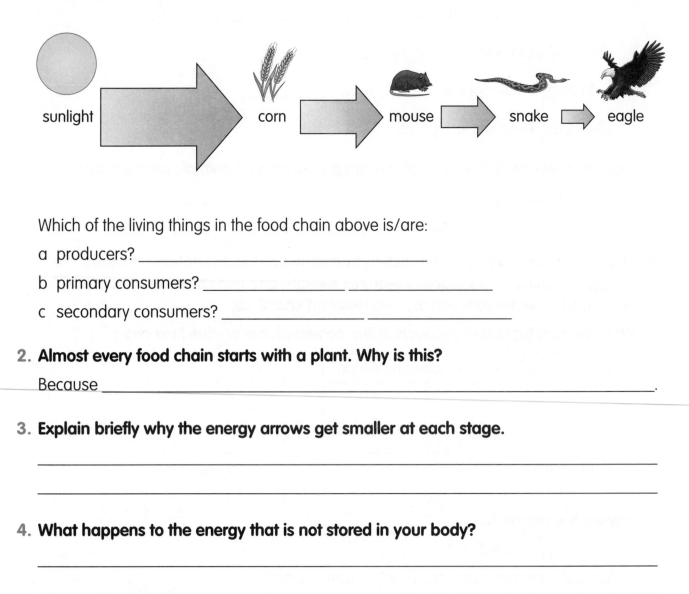

sunlight   corn   mouse   snake   eagle

Which of the living things in the food chain above is/are:

a producers? _____ _____

b primary consumers? _____ _____

c secondary consumers? _____ _____

2. **Almost every food chain starts with a plant. Why is this?**

   Because _____.

3. **Explain briefly why the energy arrows get smaller at each stage.**

   _____

   _____

4. **What happens to the energy that is not stored in your body?**

   _____

   _____

Ecosystems

1. **Unscramble the words to make sentences that describe an ecosystem.**

> community ecosystem is a of , animals organisms and smaller . plants An

_____

> itself An sustains . ecosystem

_____

Activities 2-4 refer to the diagram below, which shows an ecosystem in a bottle.

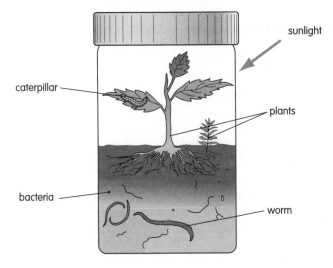

2. **Answer the questions.**

   Which of the living things in the ecosystem are:

   a producers? _____ _____

   b consumers? _____ _____

   c decomposers? _____ _____

3. **Describe briefly the importance of decomposers in an ecosystem.**

   _____

   _____

4. **Describe what would happen to the ecosystem if it were covered with a black cloth to block the sunlight.**

   _____

   _____

Threats to the environment

1. **Match the threat to the environment to the correct image. Draw lines.**

a

Oil spills

Water pollution

Waste dumping

Air pollution

Deforestation

b

c

d

e

2. **Complete the sentences with the words in the boxes.**

a (pollution   diffusion   inflation)

Harmful chemicals dumped in the environment are a form of _____.

b (homeland   waste   habitat)

Deforestation is an example of _____ destruction.

c (sources   shortages   supply)

Water misuse can lead to water _____.

d (local   global   decreasing)

Air pollution from fossil fuels is a _____ environmental problem.

3. **Describe:**

a *one* example of air pollution in your environment.

_____

_____

b *one* example of water pollution in your environment.

_____

_____

4. **Explain briefly how the pollution you described in Activity 3 affects people and other living things.**

_____

_____

Conservation

1. **Unscramble the words to make sentences about conservation.**

> conserve to care something of To that so it survive will take is .

_____

> face action human extinction . Many because is their harmed by species ecosystem

_____

2. **Unscramble the letters to find out what the Nubian ibex has become.**

> gnerendaed eciesps

_____ _____

3. **Complete the sentences with the words in the boxes.**

a   breeding   production   growing

_____ programmes are set up to increase the number of certain endangered species.

b   wastefully   wisely   plentifully

Ordinary people can contribute to conservation by using water _____.

c   efficient   consuming   transforming

Energy _____ light bulbs help conserve fuel and reduce pollution.

4. **List *four* things you can do to conserve water.**

a _____

b _____

c _____

d _____

The 3Rs — reduce, reuse, recycle

1. **Write the scientific word for each of these definitions.**

   a It describes rubbish and waste that harms the environment. _____

   b It describes materials that rot away quickly. _____

   c It describes how the materials used to make cans and bottles can be melted and used again. _____

2. **Match the lists of 'wastes' to the way you should dispose of them. Draw lines.**

   fruit peelings and other food waste   a (reuse)

   cans, bottles and newspaper   b (compost)

   empty bags and scrap paper   c (recycle)

3. **The chart below shows the results of a litter survey around a school. Use the chart to answer the questions.**

   a Which type of litter was most common? _____

   b How many pieces of plastic were found? _____

   c How many more pieces of paper were found than pieces of glass? _____

   d What was the total number of pieces of litter found? _____

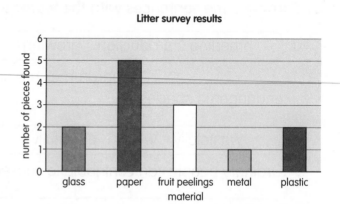

Litter survey results

4. **Walk around your environment looking for pollution. List all the different kinds of pollution you see in a table like the one below. If you can, complete the columns stating what causes the pollution, and how it could be prevented.**

Pollution observed	Caused by	Solution

End-of-unit test 1

Part A

Mark each of these sentences as true (✔) or false (✗).

1. Carbohydrates provide energy for the body. ☐

2. Sugar and butter are good sources of protein. ☐

3. 100 grams of fruit contains the same amount of energy as 100 grams of candy. ☐

4. Digested food is absorbed in the small intestine. ☐

5. Plants absorb most of their food from the soil. ☐

6. Every food chain starts with an animal. ☐

7. Governments can help protect species facing extinction. ☐

8. We can help the environment by using energy and water wisely. ☐

9. Deforestation helps to protect endangered species. ☐

10. Planting new forests will help prevent global warming. ☐

Part B

Choose the correct word to match the description.

1. [predator   carnivore   omnivore   herbivore]

   An animal that hunts other animals.

2. [acids   enzymes   sugars   vitamins]

   Chemicals in the saliva, stomach and intestines that break foods into substances the body can use.

3. [anaemic   obese   malnourished   dehydrated]

   The condition of someone who is very overweight.

Part C

Select the one correct answer for each question.

1. Which of the following is an important mineral in the diet?
   a calcium   **b** vitamin C   **c** fibre   **d** starch

2. Approximately how much water does the human body need each day?
   a 100 millilitres   **b** 500 millilitres   **c** 2.5 litres   **d** 5 litres

3. Which of these foods contains the most energy per 100 grams?
   a nuts   **b** butter   **c** bread   **d** chicken

4. Look at the diagram of the alimentary canal.

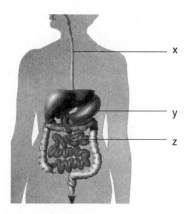

   Which of the following labels show the organs marked X, Y and Z correctly?
   a X stomach   Y gullet   Z small intestine
   b X large intestine Y small intestine   Z stomach
   c X gullet   Y stomach   Z small intestine
   d X stomach   Y small intestine   Z large intestine

5. Which one of the following does a plant not require for photosynthesis?
   a light   **b** oxygen   **c** carbon dioxide   **d** water

6. Which of these is a correct example of a food chain?
   a grass → goat → human   **b** human → goat → grass
   c goat → human → grass   **d** grass → human → goat

7. In an ecosystem the producers are:
   a plants   **b** animals   **c** microbes   **d** fungi

8. Worms, bacteria and other small living things help recycle nutrients in an ecosystem by feeding on dead things. They are:
   a consumers   **b** producers   **c** predators   **d** decomposers

9. The diagram shows an experiment to investigate photosynthesis.
   What gas is found at X?

   a nitrogen

   b carbon dioxide

   c hydrogen

   d oxygen

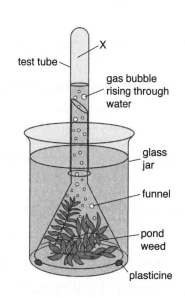

test tube

X

gas bubble rising through water

glass jar

funnel

pond weed

plasticine

10. Which one of these threats to the environment is of global significance?

    a waste dumping

    b river pollution by sewage

    c pollution of the atmosphere by burning fossil fuels

    d oil spills

Part D

Match each item in column A to the correct definition in column B.

A

1. ecosystem
2. endangered
3. conserve
4. protected area

B

a An environment that is protected by law.

b To care for something so that it will survive into the future.

c Species that are threatened with extinction.

d A community of living things in one place that sustains itself.

Part E

Explain in a few sentences:

1. The importance of eating a balanced diet.
2. Why fresh fruit and vegetables are healthy foods.
3. The three bin system for disposing of waste.
4. Why plants are called producers and animals consumers.
5. Some ways in which human actions harm the environment.

Elements, compounds and mixtures

1. **Match the words to their definitions. Write each word in the correct space.**

   | atom   element   compound   mixture |

   a A substance in which the atoms of two or more elements are joined together.
   _____

   b A combination of two or more substances that are jumbled together but have not reacted chemically. _____

   c The smallest unit (particle) that makes up an element. _____

   d A substance composed of just one type of atom. _____

2. **Find the ten elements in this word square.**

s	p	r	s	i	l	v	e	r
u	t	i	g	o	l	d	w	l
r	g	e	o	d	p	u	s	z
a	l	u	m	i	n	i	u	m
f	e	w	a	n	r	r	l	e
c	o	p	p	e	r	o	p	e
l	o	x	y	g	e	n	h	u
o	c	a	r	b	o	n	u	n
e	t	m	e	r	c	u	r	y

3. Match the symbols to the elements you found in Activity 2.

Write the names of these elements and their symbols in the table below.

Al   S   O   Fe   C   Hg   Au   Ag   I

element name	symbol

4. Look at these drawings of particles in gases. Label each gas as an element, a mixture or a compound.

a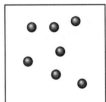

b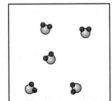

c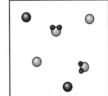

_____   _____   _____

Physical and chemical changes

1. Match the words to the definitions. Write the words in the correct spaces.

> physical change   reversed   chemical change   permanent   react

a A change in which atoms and molecules react and new substances are formed.
_____

b Sent backwards or undone. _____

c Something that is long lasting or unchanging. _____

d When two or more substances combine to make a new substance or substances.
_____

e A change to a substance that does not involve a chemical reaction.
_____

2. Mark each of these statements as true (✔) or false (✗).

a A physical change is easily reversed. ☐

b Burning is a physical change. ☐

c A chemical change is permanent. ☐

d Melting is a chemical change. ☐

3. Match the reactions to the correct type of change: chemical or physical. Draw lines.

a (wood burning)

b (wax melting)

c (water freezing)

d (concrete setting)

e (vinegar and baking soda reacting)

f (bread baking)

g (egg frying)

h (water boiling)

(physical change)

(chemical change)

4. Describe briefly how you could reverse each of these changes.

a Ice lolly melting in the heat of the sun. _____
_____

b Dissolving salt in water. _____
_____

c Water boiling to make steam. _____
_____

Mixtures and solutions

1. **Match the words to the definitions. Write the words in the correct spaces.**

   dissolve   suspension   solution   pure

   a Describes a single substance, not mixed with anything else. _____

   b When the basic particles of a substance separate to become part of a solution.

      _____

   c A mixture in which the particles of a solid spread out so well, they seem to 'vanish' into a liquid. _____

   d A cloudy mixture of solid particles in a liquid. _____

   Activities 2-4 refer to the experiment described below.

   Richard and Ali are comparing the dissolving times of different sugar samples in warm water and cold water.

   They stir each sample into the water and record the number of seconds until it is completely dissolved.

   These are their results.

Sugar sample	Time to dissolve (seconds) Cold water (10°C)	Warm water (40°C)
large crystals	93	49
granules	71	38
powder (icing sugar)	62	32

2. **List the things Richard and Ali should do to make sure their comparisons are fair.**

   a _____

   b _____

   c _____

3. **Write down *two* conclusions Richard and Ali can form from their results.**

   a _____

   b _____

4. **Suggest an explanation for the observations made in this experiment.**

   _____

   _____

Separating mixtures

1. **Label each separation method using the words in the box.**

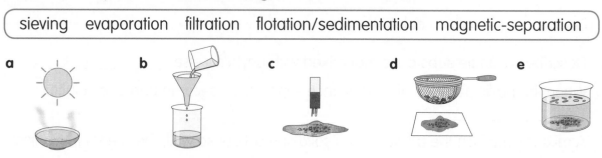

| sieving | evaporation | filtration | flotation/sedimentation | magnetic-separation |

a _____   b _____   c _____   d _____   e _____

2. **Select the best method from those shown in Activity 1 to make the separations listed in this table. Write the methods in the table.**

Separation	Method
iron filings from brass filings	
wood chips from stones	
salt from seawater	
sand from gravel	
sand from water	

3. **Describe a separation method you might use in the kitchen when making a drink or cooking.**

_____

_____

_____

_____

4. **You are provided with a mixture of sand and salt, a container of water, a funnel and filter paper, a collecting jar and a shallow dish. List the steps you would take to separate the salt from the sand.**

_____

_____

_____

_____

The properties of water

1. **Match the word box on the left to the box on the right to make a complete sentence. Draw lines. Each sentence should state a property of water.**

The mass of one litre of water	**a** (at 100° C.)
When heated, water boils	**b** (is one kilogram.)
Ice melts	**c** (smell or taste.)
Pure water has no colour	**d** (at 0°C.)

2. **Mark each of these statements as true (✔) or false (✗).**

   a Water in the solid state is called ice. ☐

   b The normal state of water in a warm country such as Egypt is solid. ☐

   c There is more water in your body than any other substance. ☐

   d Water is the only substance on Earth commonly found as a solid, a liquid and a gas. ☐

3. **Unscramble these words to make five properties of liquid water.
   (If you are stuck look at this topic in your Pupil's Book for possible words.)**

   transapentr   incompribleess   lessourcol

   wflso   ventols

   _____ _____ _____ _____ _____

4. **Make a boat**

    You will a need: bowl, water, wood or thick card, scissors, soap.
   Instructions:
   - Fill a bowl with fresh water.
   - Cut a small boat shape from wood or thick card as shown.
   - Press a small piece of soap into the notch at the back of the boat.
   - Lower the boat on to the water surface.

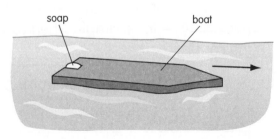

soap   boat

The soap reduces the surface tension of the water at the back of the boat. The surface tension of the water at the front of the boat pulls it forward through the water.

Using water

1. **Unscramble the letters to make six different uses for water.**
   (If you are stuck look at this topic in your Pupil's Book for possible words.)

   krgidnin

   annasitiot

   oncuircialt

   _____

   _____

   _____

   trsonatnaporti

   snghfii

   rdinusty

   _____

   _____

   _____

2. **Mark each of these statements as true (✔) or false (✗).**

   a Water is the most common substance in the bodies of living things. ☐

   b Tropical forests are very dry. ☐

   c There is more fresh water than salt water on the Earth's surface. ☐

   d Sea water contains too much salt for irrigating crops. ☐

3. **Match the words to the definitions. Write the words in the correct spaces.**

   drought   famine   desert   irrigation

   a A food shortage when there is not enough to eat to stay healthy. _____

   b A long period with no rain. _____

   c Providing water artificially to growing crops. _____

   d An environment with very little rain. _____

4. **List the ways you use water directly and indirectly.**

   (*Direct* uses are when you touch or handle the water you use — drinking and washing
   for example. *Indirect* uses are when you do not see or handle the water, but water is still
   necessary — for example when you eat bread you are using the water needed to grow
   the corn.)

Direct uses of water	Indirect uses of water

The properties of air

1. **Which one of the following describes air? Tick (✔) the one correct answer.**

   a rigid, strong and heavy

   b visible, dense and stiff

   c transparent, thin and light

   d weightless and poisonous

2. **A girl turns a plastic cup upside down (A), and pushes it under the surface of some water in a bowl (B). Answer the questions.**

   (If you are not sure of the answers, then try the experiment yourself.)

A 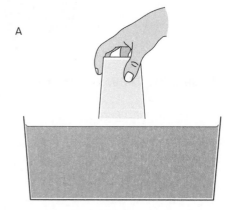   B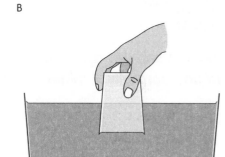

   a What is inside the cup in position B? _____

   b Explain why the cup does not fill with water.

   _____

   c Draw and describe what happens if the girl now tilts the cup on to its side.

   _____

   _____

3. **This diagram shows two toy balloons filled with air. They are hanging from a balance. One of the balloons is pricked with a pin and the air escapes. What happens to the balance? Make a drawing to show how it will appear.**

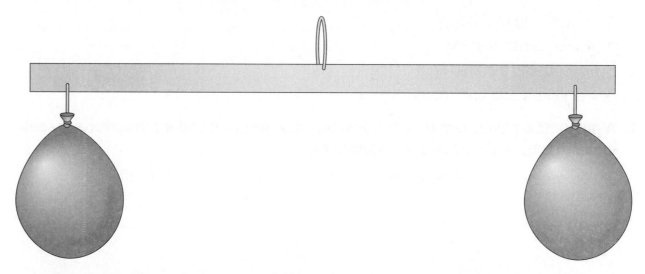

4. **A student used this apparatus to observe how much air they blew out when breathing normally. Explain how it works.**

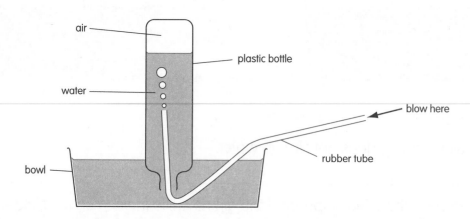

5. **Measure how much air your lungs contain.**

 You will need: a bowl, water, a 2 litre plastic bottle, about 30 cm of plastic or rubber tube.

Instructions:
- Fill a bowl with water.
- Fill a two-litre plastic bottle with water.
- With your thumb over the top, invert the bottle in the bowl as shown.
- Remove your thumb from the top.
- Slide one end of the piece of plastic or rubber tube into the water and up into the neck of the bottle.
- Take a deep breath and blow into the rubber tube, emptying the air from your lungs into the bottle. If you can fill the bottle with air, your lungs must hold at least two litres.

What's in the air?

1. This bar chart shows the composition of the air. Draw lines to match the gases named to the correct part of the chart.

nitrogen   oxygen   argon, carbon dioxide and other gases

0%   100%

2. Read this article.

This was a headline in the newspaper.

Family overcome by fumes from gas cooker.
Investigator blames poor ventilation.

We need oxygen from fresh air to breathe. Ventilation (open doors, windows and air vents) lets fresh air in and stale air out. Lighting a gas or charcoal burner in a room without ventilation is very dangerous. Many people have died through making this mistake.

Look at these pictures. Answer the questions.

a Which room is safe? _____

b Which room is dangerous? _____

c Which gas from the air do we need to breathe? _____

d Why does lighting a flame make the air stale? _____

3. **The candle inside this jar has just been lit.**

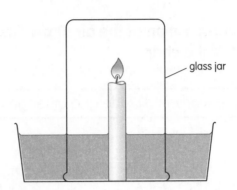

glass jar

    a Mark the level of the water in the jar when the candle goes out.

    b Explain why the candle does not keep burning.

    _____

    _____

4. **Answer the questions.**

Use the library or the Internet to find two uses for each of the following gases that form the air.

    a nitrogen. _____ _____

    b oxygen. _____ _____

    c carbon dioxide. _____ _____

    d Name the scientist who discovered each gas.

    _____

    _____

    _____

Using gases from the air

1. **Write the gas for each of these descriptions. Use each gas name twice.**

   oxygen   nitrogen   carbon dioxide

   a The gas we need to breathe. _____

   b The most common gas in the air. _____

   c The gas that gives drinks their fizz. _____

   d The gas that supports burning. _____

   e A gas used to make fertilizer. _____

   f   A gas used in fire extinguishers. _____

2. **Explain briefly how the different gases in air can be separated.**

   _____

   _____

3. **What do you breathe out?**

   During respiration your body produces carbon dioxide as a waste gas. You excrete this gas from your body when you breathe out.

    You will need: limewater (a solution of calcium hydroxide), a straw, a large test tube.

   blow here

   straw

   lime water

   Instructions:

   • Blow through the straw so that the air from your lungs bubbles through the limewater.

   The limewater becomes milky. This is the standard test for carbon dioxide.

4. **A teacher prepares covered jars of three different gases. She performs the following tests on each gas.**

   Test 1 — she drops a lighted match into a jar and covers it again.

   Test 2 — she adds a little limewater to a jar, covers the jar and shakes it.

   This table gives the results of these tests. Write the name of the gas in the table.

	Gas A	Gas B	Gas C
Test 1	Match extinguished	Match burns more brightly	Match extinguished
Test 2	Limewater turns cloudy	No effect	No effect
name of gas			

End-of-unit test 2

Part A

Mark each of these statements as true (✔) or false (✗).

1. A physical change can be reversed. ☐

2. Burning is a physical change. ☐

3. In a chemical change new substances are produced. ☐

4. Insects can walk on water because of surface tension. ☐

5. The mass of one litre of water is 100 grams. ☐

6. Seawater can be used for irrigation. ☐

7. Living things are mainly composed of water. ☐

8. Water is transparent. ☐

9. Air is weightless. ☐

10. Air takes up space. ☐

11. Air exerts pressure. ☐

Part B

Choose the correct word or words to match the description.

1. ┌───┐
   │ physical change   chemical change   permanent change │
   └───┘

   A change to a substance in which new substances are not formed. This type of change can easily be reversed.

2. ┌───┐
   │   react   burn   dissolve   evaporate   │
   └───┘

   When the particles of a substance spread throughout a liquid to become part of a solution.

3. ┌───┐
   │   nitrogen   oxygen   carbon dioxide   argon   │
   └───┘

   The gas that supports respiration and combustion (burning).

Part C

Tick (✔) the one correct answer for each question.

1. Which one of the following is a compound?
   a oxygen
   b water
   c iron
   d sulphur

2. Which sugar sample will dissolve fastest?

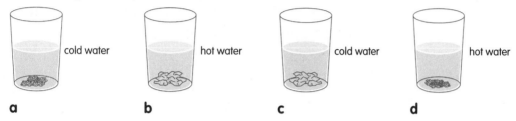

cold water   hot water   cold water   hot water

  a   **b**   **c**   **d**

3. Select a method for separating a mixture of sand and water and recovering both components:
   a filtration
   b evaporation
   c freezing
   d using a magnet

4. A cloudy mixture of chalk and water is a:
   a solution
   b solvent
   c solid
   d suspension

5. Which of the following is not an important use for water in the body?
   a digestion
   b cooling
   c relaxation
   d excretion

6. Air is a mixture of gases. Which component of air do we use to make fertilizers?
   a carbon dioxide
   b nitrogen
   c argon
   d water vapour

Part D

Match each item in column A to the correct definition in column B.

A

1. element
2. compound
3. mixture
4. atom

B

a A substance in which the atoms of two or more elements are joined together.

b The smallest unit (particle) that makes up an element.

c A liquid in which a solid dissolves.

d A substance composed of just one type of atom.

e A combination of two or more substances that are jumbled together, but have not reacted chemically.

Part E

Explain in a few sentences:

1. Why a candle burning in a closed jar goes out
2. The differences between a physical change and a chemical change
3. How you could separate a mixture of sand and salt
4. The difference between a suspension and a solution
5. How you can show that air has weight

Water from different sources

1. **Find the ten different places from which you might take water in this word square.**

b	o	t	t	l	e	a	q
o	d	f	a	q	r	w	d
r	z	x	p	i	p	e	s
e	c	v	b	n	m	l	t
h	s	r	a	i	n	l	r
o	f	g	p	u	m	p	e
l	a	k	e	h	j	k	a
e	v	c	a	n	a	l	m

2. **Mark each of these statements as true (✔) or false (✗).**

   a Water from some sources may be polluted with germs. ☐

   b Polluted water spreads disease. ☐

   c Water can be made safe by boiling or by treating it with chemicals. ☐

   d It is safe to drink water straight from a river or a canal. ☐

3. **It is only safe to drink water from one of these sources. Tick (✔) the one correct answer.**

   a lake water

   b bottled water

   c river water

   d well water

Lesson 1

4. How can water be purified?

Sometimes we must use water from sources that may not be safe. Then we must *purify* the water. Try this investigation to see how water can be purified.

 You will need: water from a river or pond, a water filter (clean white cotton cloth), plastic containers, a cooking pot or kettle, a stove or hot plate.

Instructions:

Look carefully at your water sample. Is it clean or dirty? Can you see any particles in it?

- Now filter the water. You can do this by pouring it through a clean cotton cloth.
- Examine the water after filtering. Is it clearer than before?
- Look at the cloth. Has anything been trapped in it?

Filtering removes small particles of dirt from the water. But the water is still not safe. It may contain germs (microbes). Germs are small enough to pass through a filter.

To make the water safe you must boil it. Boiling kills germs.

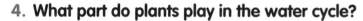

The water cycle

1. A pupil places a dish of water in a hot sunny place. She marks the water level with a pen. Make marks on the diagram to predict the water level in the dish after:

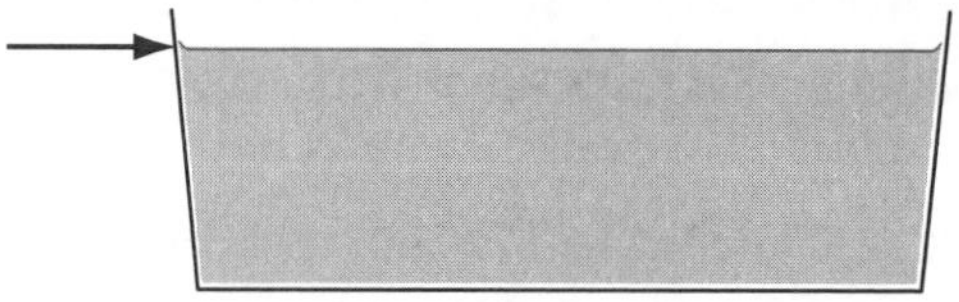

a 30 minutes in the sun

b 6 hours in the sun

Explain what happens to the water that was in the dish at the start of the investigation.

____

____

2. The air conditioning in an apartment is turned up high and the rooms are very cool. Someone leaves a kettle boiling in the kitchen. Answer the questions.

a What happens to the mirrors and windows in the apartment?

____

b Explain your answer.

____

3. Look at the diagram of the water cycle. What is the correct sequence indicated by 1, 2 and 3? Tick (✓) the one correct answer.

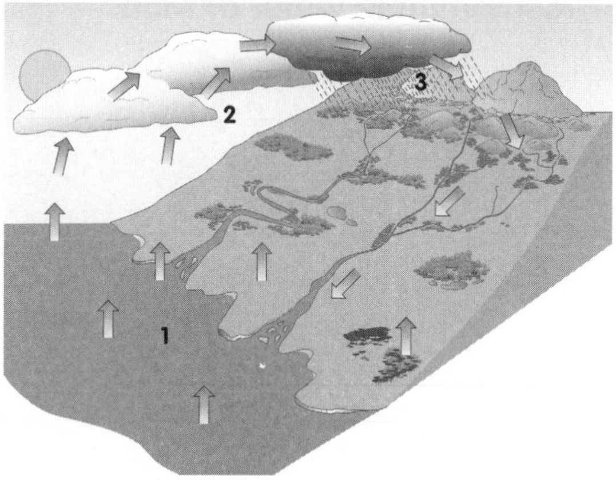

a evaporation, condensation, rainfall

b rainfall, condensation, evaporation

c evaporation, rainfall, condensation

d condensation, evaporation, rainfall

4. What part do plants play in the water cycle?

Perform this investigation to prove that plants take water from the soil and release it into the air.

You will need: a pot plant, a clear plastic bag.

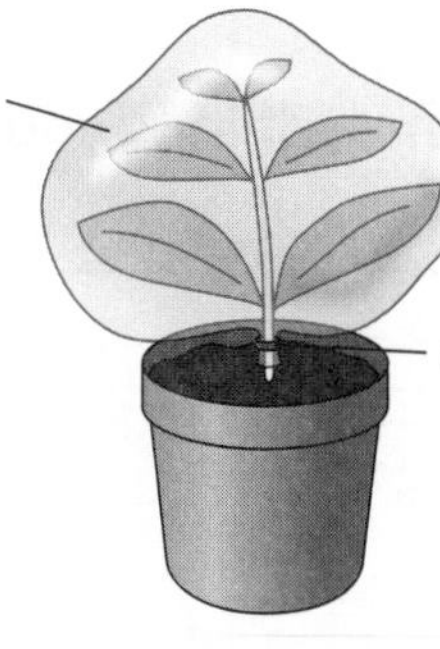

Instructions:

- Water the plant, then cover it with the plastic bag as shown.
- Stand the plant in a sunny place.
- After several hours observe the inside of the bag.
  What do you see? Has the plant lost water through its leaves?

Water and disease

1. Unscramble the letters to make five waterborne diseases.
(If you are stuck look at this topic in your Pupil's Book for possible words.)

(pyhtoid) (olchera) (olpio) (athetipis) (harzbiali)

_____   _____   _____   _____   _____

2. Match the following diseases to the symptoms. Write in the spaces given.

(bilharzia   hepatitis A   cholera   poliomyelitis   typhoid)

a Headache, high temperature, sickness and diarrhoea. _____

b Sudden sickness and diarrhoea. _____

c Fever, bad headache, pain and stiffness of neck and back. _____

d Yellow skin, tiredness, fever. _____

e Blood in urine, tiredness. _____

3. Draw and label *two* ways in which germs that cause waterborne diseases may contaminate water or food.

4. List *three* things you can do to avoid catching and/or spreading waterborne diseases.

a _____

b _____

c _____

Purifying water

1. **Match the words to the descriptions. Write the words in the correct spaces.**

   chlorine   germs   filter   purify   boil

   a To make germ free and clean. _____

   b To remove dirt or impurities; a device for doing this. _____

   c To heat water to 100 °C — the temperature at which it bubbles and changes to steam.
      _____

   d Very small living things that may contaminate food or water and cause disease.
      _____

   e A chemical that can kill germs in water. _____

   Activities 2–4 refer to this diagram of a water treatment plant.

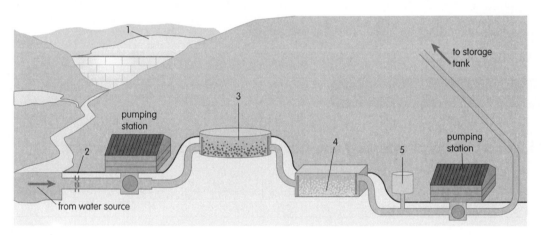

2. **Label the numbered parts of the treatment plant using the correct word(s).**

   chlorination plant   filter bed   grid   settlement tank   reservoir

3. **Write the name of the part of the plant for each of these descriptions.**

   a Where fine particles and microbes are trapped in sand. _____

   b Where chemicals are added to make small particles settle. _____

4. **Briefly describe the purpose of:**

   a the grid.

   _____

   b the chlorination plant.

   _____

Conserving water

1. Match the words to the descriptions. Write the words in the correct spaces.

> misuse   conserve   desalination

a Separating fresh water from seawater. _____

b To care for something: to prevent from being harmed or wasted. _____

c To waste, spoil or harm something. _____

2. Match the item to the amount of water used. Draw lines.

Leaving a tap running for 10 minutes   **a** (10–25)

Taking a shower   **b** (100)

Taking a bath   **c** (50)

An average person's daily water use   **d** (80)

3. Draw and label a picture of *one* way you have seen people misusing water.

4. List *five* things you can do to conserve water.

a _____

b _____

c _____

d _____

e _____

The atmosphere

1. **Mark each of these statements as true (✔) or false (✗).**

   a The force of gravity holds the atmosphere around the Earth. ☐

   b Oxygen is the most abundant (common) gas in the atmosphere. ☐

   c Most of the air that makes up the atmosphere is within 30 kilometres of the Earth's surface. ☐

   d The higher you rise in the atmosphere, the hotter it gets. ☐

2. **The atmosphere contains water vapour. Explain briefly:**

   a What causes water vapour to enter the atmosphere?

   _____

   _____

   b What becomes of this water vapour as hot air rises?

   _____

   _____

3. **Label these clouds using the words in the box.**

   (cumulus   stratus   cirrus)

   a _____   b _____   c _____

4. **Match the cloud names to their meanings. Draw lines.**

cumulus		a	clouds are high in the atmosphere
stratus		b	clouds are fluffy fair weather clouds
cirrus		c	clouds form in layers

Air pollution

1. **Find the ten sources and types of air pollution in this word square.**

c	o	n	s	t	r	u	c	t	i	o	n
c	h	e	m	i	c	a	l	s	t	u	e
g	h	r	o	r	s	e	s	y	o	s	n
h	o	u	g	s	o	o	f	g	i	e	m
f	a	c	t	o	r	i	e	s	n	f	o
i	q	u	a	r	r	i	e	s	s	u	d
r	t	o	n	i	l	i	n	g	e	m	u
e	n	t	e	v	e	h	i	c	l	e	s
s	m	o	k	i	n	g	l	e	h	s	t

Activities 2–4 are about the investigation below.

Richard and Ali investigated dust pollution around the school. They smeared petroleum jelly on microscope slides, then placed the slides in different locations.

The locations were: next to a busy road; the playground; a classroom; the medical room. After 24 hours they collected the slides and examined them with a low power microscope. This is what they saw.

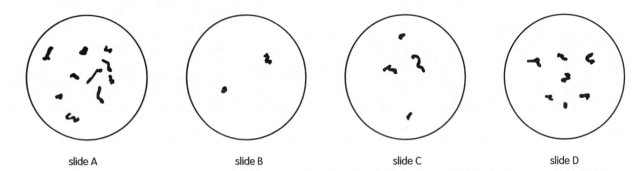

slide A   slide B   slide C   slide D

2. Make a list of the number of dust particles observed on each slide. Complete the table.

	Number of particles	Possible location
slide A		
slide B		
slide C		
slide D		

3. Answer the questions.

a Which locations were the different slides collected from?

_____

_____

b Explain your ideas.

_____

_____

_____

_____

4. Use the data in the table to draw a block graph of the results.

Cleaning the air

1. **Answer the questions.**

   a What is the purpose of an air filter?

   _____

   b Explain briefly how an air filter works.

   _____

2. **Unscramble these words to make *four* things which have air filters.**
   (If you are stuck look at this topic in your Pupil's Book for possible words.)

   acr nnegie

   _____ _____

   mpocuter

   _____

   torfacy mnchiey

   _____ _____

   cuvaum ecleanr

   _____ _____

3. **Why do the things in Activity 2 have air filters? Explain the purpose of the filter in each case.**

   a _____

   _____

   b _____

   _____

   c _____

   _____

   d _____

   _____

4. **Answer the questions.**

   a What does the picture show? _____

   b Why should you wear a mask like this on a construction site?

   _____

   _____

Global warming

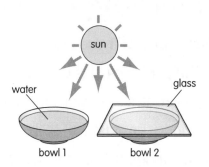

1. **This diagram shows an experiment to investigate the greenhouse effect. Answer the questions.**

   a In which bowl does the water get hotter?

   _____

   b Explain why.

   _____

2. **This diagram shows how gases in the upper atmosphere trap heat. The layer of gas acts like the glass in a greenhouse.**

   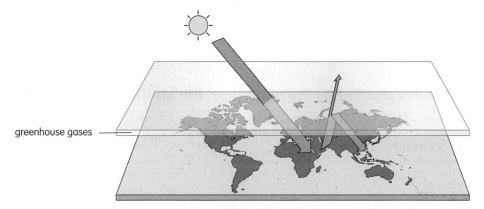

   Give *two* reasons why the amounts of greenhouse gases in the atmosphere are increasing.

   a _____

   b _____

3. **If more heat is trapped in the atmosphere, how will the Earth's temperature change? Mark this statements as true (✔) or false (✗).**

   a It will rise. ☐

   b It will fall. ☐

4. **What are the consequences of global warming? Mark each of these statements as true (✔) or false (✗).**

   a lower temperatures ☐

   b stronger winds ☐

   c more droughts ☐

   d falling sea levels ☐

The changing Earth

1. **Mark each of these statements as true (✔) or false (✗).**

   a The Earth's crust is broken into 14 main plates. ☐

   b The Earth's plates are moving. ☐

   c During the past 200 million years the continents have drifted closer together. ☐

   d Volcanoes and earthquakes are more common at the centres of the plates, away from plate boundaries. ☐

2. **Explain briefly what causes the Earth's plates to move.**

   _____

   _____

   _____

3. **Label these features created by movements of the Earth's plates using the words in the box.**

   ┌─────────────────────────────┐
   │ fault   rift   mountains │
   └─────────────────────────────┘

   a

   b

   c

   _____   _____   _____

   _____   _____   _____

4. **Which ways do the plates move to create these features? Draw arrows on the diagrams in Activity 3 (the third example has been completed for you). Write these labels under the diagrams they describe.**

   ┌──┐
   │ plates collide   plates slip   plates move apart │
   └──┘

Volcanoes

1. **Mark each of these statements as true (✔) or false (✗).**

a Molten rock below the ground is called lava. ☐

b Rift volcanoes form where the Earth's plates pull apart. ☐

c Subduction volcanoes form where an ocean plate collides with a continental plate. ☐

d Rift volcanoes are more explosive than subduction volcanoes. ☐

2. **Label the features of this volcano. Use the words in the box.**

> crater   gas and ash   magma   lava

a _____

b _____

c _____

d _____

3. **Match the words to the descriptions. Write the words in the correct spaces.**

> crater   erupt   magma   evacuate

a When everyone in an area leaves their homes and moves away to avoid danger.
_____

b When molten rock, gas and ash break through the Earth's crust. _____

c Hot molten rock under the ground. _____

d A large bowl shaped hole. _____

4. **Describe *three* observations scientists can make to help predict when a volcano will erupt.**

a _____

b _____

c _____

The rock cycle

1. **Unscramble these words to make three types of rock.**
   (If you are stuck look at this topic in the Pupil's Book for possible words.)

   nigeous

   _____   _____   _____

2. **Match each rock type in Activity 1 to the description of its formation. Write the correct words in the correct spaces.**

   a Buried rock is changed by heat and pressure. _____

   b Weathered rock particles are deposited in layers and stick together.

      _____

   c Molten magma rises and cools. _____

3. **Write these processes in the correct places in the rock cycle. You will need to use each group of words twice.**

   | weathering, erosion and sedimentation | melting, cooling | heat, pressure |

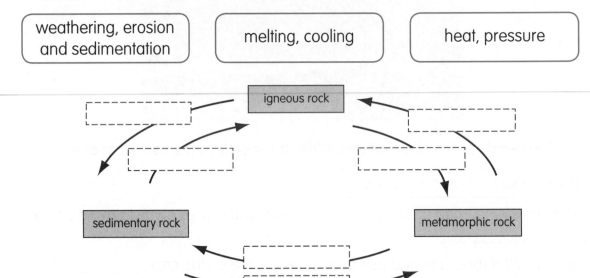

4. **Which sequence could transform igneous rocks first to sedimentary rocks, and then to metamorphic rock? Tick (✔) the one correct answer.**

   a transformation by heat and pressure-uplift-weathering-erosion

   b melting-cooling-weathering-erosion-sedimentation

   c weathering-erosion-sedimentation-transformation by heat and pressure

   d sedimentation-transformation by heat and pressure-melting

Earthquakes

1. Match the earthquake words to the definitions. Write the words in the correct spaces.

> focus   epicentre   Richter scale   magnitude

a A scale for reporting the strength of an earthquake. _____

b The point underground at the centre of an earthquake. _____

c A number that measures the strength of an earthquake. _____

d The point on the ground immediately above the focus of an earthquake. _____

2. Write these descriptions of earthquakes in the correct sequence on the Richter scale.

> Great   Minor   Moderate   Very minor   Light
> Major   Micro   Strong

Magnitude	Description
1	
2	
3	
4	
5	
6	
7	
8+	

3. Write your estimate of the magnitude for each of these earthquakes.

a Significant damage to old and poorly built houses. _____

b Recorded but not felt. _____

c Widespread destruction of a great city. _____

d Plates and cups rattle, but no significant damage. _____

4. **Discuss which would be safer in an earthquake — a stone house with shallow foundations and heavy roof tiles or a wooden house with deep foundations and a straw roof.**

_____

_____

_____

Draw and label a design for an earthquake-resistant home.

Earthquakes and people

1. Mark each of these statements as true (✔) or false (✗).

In an earthquake you should:

a Run outdoors. ☐

b Shelter under a table. ☐

c Stay away from glass or anything that could fall. ☐

d Cover your face. ☐

2. Explain briefly why, following an earthquake, you should *not*:

a Shout for help if you are trapped under debris.

_____

b Light a match.

_____

c Move about to try and get free.

_____

d Leave your vehicle.

_____

3. Answer the questions.

a What is a tsunami?

_____

b How is it caused?

_____

4. Earthquakes cannot be predicted, but an early warning can be given of a tsunami. Explain why this is possible.

_____

_____

_____

Lesson 15

Shaping the landscape

1. **Find the *five* forces that change the landscape in this word square.**

m	o	v	i	n	g	p	l	a	t	e	s
w	s	o	t	o	d	u	p	u	l	k	s
u	k	l	e	k	e	s	d	o	k	r	t
i	l	c	e	w	i	n	d	l	e	s	r
c	r	a	t	a	l	l	y	c	i	p	e
k	u	n	d	t	r	o	d	a	e	r	t
l	a	o	m	e	b	b	i	h	g	s	c
y	h	e	a	r	t	h	q	u	a	k	e

2. **List these forces in order of speed of onslaught, with the most sudden first and the most gradual last.**

	Speed of onslaught	Force
1 (fastest)		
2		
3		
4		
5 (slowest)		

3. **Draw a diagram to show how the forces shown could cause the Earth's crust to fold.**

4. **In the diagrams how will the water change the cliff and how will the wind and sand change the rock pillar?**

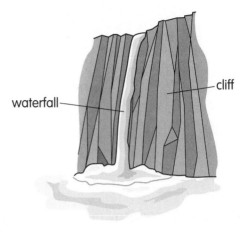

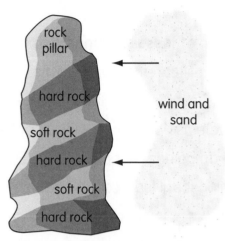

a The cliff will

_____ .

b The rock pillar will

_____ .

Draw pictures of the effects of these forces over many years.

End-of-unit test 3

Part A

Mark each of these statements as true (✔) or false (✘).

1. A water filter removes all germs from water. ☐

2. Germs in water are killed by boiling. ☐

3. All water is boiled before it is supplied to a town or city. ☐

4. Human beings cannot affect the Earth's climate. ☐

5. Burning fossil fuels contributes to global warming. ☐

6. To prevent climate change we should use oil instead of solar energy. ☐

7. We can reduce global warming by cutting down forests. ☐

8. In an earthquake the best place to shelter is outside by a wall. ☐

9. If there is an earthquake when you are at school you should shelter under a table or desk. ☐

10. The Earth's crust is broken into plates. ☐

Part B

Choose the correct word to match the description.

1. [cumulus   stratus   cirrus   nimbus]

   Fluffy, white 'fair weather' clouds.

2. [argon   nitrogen   oxygen   carbon dioxide]

   A greenhouse gas.

3. [sedimentary   igneous   metamorphic   fossil]

   The type of rock formed when magma cools.

Part C

Select the one correct answer for each question.

1. The clouds shown are best described as:

   a cumulus

   b stratus

   c cirrus

   d nimbus

2. Look at the diagram of the water cycle. What is the correct sequence indicated by 1, 2, 3?

   a evaporation, condensation, rainfall

   b rainfall, condensation, evaporation

   c evaporation, rainfall, condensation

   d condensation, evaporation, rainfall

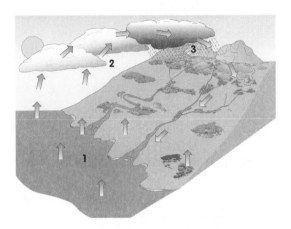

3. It is only safe to drink water from one of these sources. Which is it?

   a lake water

   b bottled water

   c river water

   d well water

4. What is the main cause of the spread of waterborne diseases such as typhoid and cholera?

   a treating water with chlorine

   b boiling water before drinking it

   c minerals dissolved in water

   d contamination of water supplies with human waste

5. At which locations on the Earth are volcanoes and earthquakes most likely?

   a A and B

   b C and D

   c E and F

   d G and H

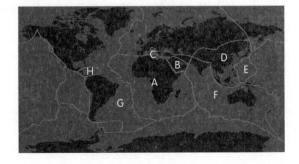

6. Which combination of forces produced the fault shown?

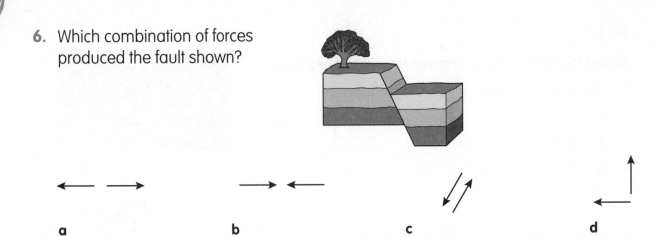

a   b   c   d

Part D

Match the words in column A to the correct definitions in column B.

A
1. rock cycle
2. plate boundary
3. fault
4. rift

B
a   A line along which two plates of the Earth's crust meet.
b   A line along which parts of the Earth's crust have slipped relative to each other.
c   The space created when two of the Earth's plates that were joined move apart.
d   A weakness in the Earth's crust through which magma flows.
e   The geological processes that are continuously transforming one type of rock into another.

Part E

Explain in a few sentences:
1. The differences between hard water and soft water
2. What aquifers are, and why they are important in some countries
3. How you can conserve water
4. How mountains are created
5. What causes an earthquake

Types of motion

1. **Match the type of motion to the description. Write the words in the correct spaces.**

   > translation   oscillation   rotation

   a Repeated to-and-fro movement. _____

   b Turning motion around an axle. _____

   c Motion in a straight line. _____

2. **Write the name of the type of motion under each picture.**

   a

   b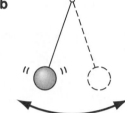

   c

   _____   _____   _____

3. **Draw or name examples of the following rides at the funfair or play park.**

   A ride that oscillates   A ride that rotates   A ride in which you
                                                                 move along a line

   _____   _____   _____

4. **Match the mechanism to the way it is being used to change motion. Draw lines.**

   a

   b

   c

   > rotation → oscillation   oscillation → rotation   rotation → translation

Forces and their effects

1. Draw an arrow to show the direction of the force on each of these things. Write push or pull on the line under each force.

a   b   c   d

_____ _____ _____ _____

2. Match these sentences to the name of the force they describe. Draw lines.

The force that warms your hands when you rub them	a gravity
The force that pulls things to the ground	b magnetic force
The force you feel when you stretch elastic	c friction
The force that attracts a steel ball to a magnet	d elastic force

3. Friction makes moving things slow down. The greater the friction the faster things slow. A pupil investigates the force of friction on a coin moving on different surfaces. He flicks the coin with a ruler, and measures how far it travels.

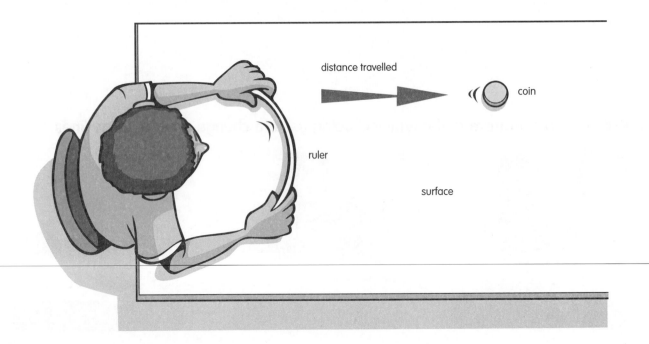

distance travelled

coin

ruler

surface

Forces and energy: Motion, forces and machines

He records his results on a bar chart.

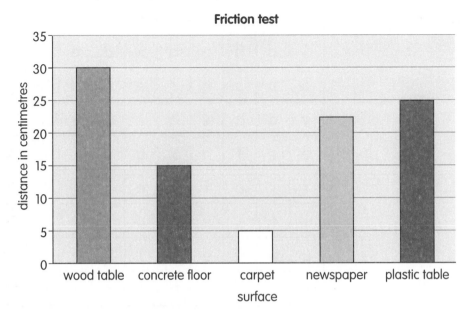

Friction test

Answer the questions.

a Which surface had most friction? _____

b Which surface had least friction? _____

4. **Carry out your own investigation of friction like the one described in Activity 3. Think carefully about how you can make your investigation fair. Answer the questions.**

a How can you use the ruler to give the same size force in each test?

_____

b Why must all the surfaces be level?

_____

c Why must you use the same coin for each test?

_____

d Why is it a good idea to repeat each test two or three times?

_____

_____

Simple machines

1. **Find ten machines and tools in this grid.**

n	u	t	c	r	a	c	k	e	r
l	a	h	p	q	x	d	e	y	o
e	b	s	c	r	e	w	d	i	f
v	a	b	c	b	r	s	r	f	j
e	r	t	a	k	g	g	i	c	x
r	r	o	l	l	e	r	l	h	n
i	o	j	v	p	u	l	l	e	y
u	w	h	e	e	l	k	e	d	m
s	p	a	n	n	e	r	l	w	z

2. **Match these machines to the job that they do.**

> lever   wheel   single pulley

a Changes the direction of a force. _____

b Increases the strength of a force or the distance of movement. _____

c Makes the transportation of loads easier. _____

3. **Identify four simple machines you use in the home or at school.**
State the purpose of each machine and describe how it makes the task easier.

Machine	Purpose	How it makes the task easier

Levers

1. **Match these lever words to their definitions.**

   load   effort   pivot

   a The point about which a lever turns. _____

   b The force which the lever overcomes. _____

   c The force applied to work a lever. _____

2. **Label this lever.**

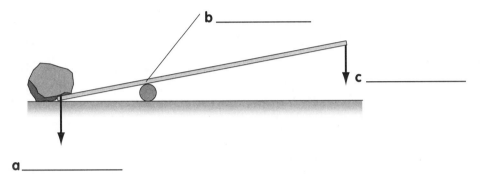

3. **The loads are identical. Which is easiest to lift? Explain why**

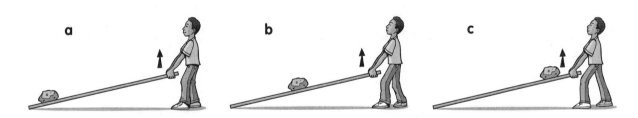

_____

4. **Your body is a machine made from different levers linked together.**

   This diagram shows how your biceps muscle
   bends your arm at the elbow to lift a ball.

   From the diagram identify:

   a the load   _____

   b the pivot   _____

   c the lever   _____

   d the source of the effort   _____

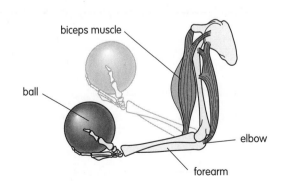

Pulleys

1. **Mark each of these statements as true (✔) or false (✗).**

   a A single pulley can change the direction of a force from down to up. ☐

   b With two pulleys you need twice as much force to raise a load. ☐

   c With three pulleys you can raise three times the load with the same force. ☐

   d With four pulleys the load would rise four times further than with a single pulley. ☐

   Questions 2-4 are about the pulleys shown in this diagram.

   a   b   c

2. **The rope is missing from set of pulleys B. Draw it in place to show how the pulleys should be connected.**

3. **Which way must you pull the rope ends to raise the loads? Draw arrows.**

4. **Which load will be easiest to raise?**

   _____

   Which load will be hardest to raise?

   _____

   Explain your answers

   _____

   _____

Screws

1. Unscramble these words to find seven items with screw threads.

oecrkcsrw   lrdil   lbot   odwo secrw

_____   _____   _____   _____

vcei   acr acjk   tobtle acp

_____   _____   _____

2. Label the parts of this screw. Use the words below.

thread   pitch

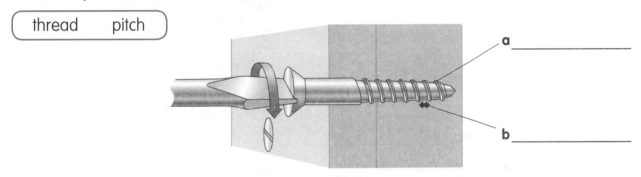

a _____

b _____

3. The pitch of the screw shown in Activity 2 is 2 mm. How far will the screw move into the wood if the screwdriver makes five complete rotations?

_____

Explain your answer.

_____

_____

4. Mark each of these statements as true (✔) or false (✗).

a A screw multiplies the effort used to turn it.   ☐

b One turn of a screw moves it forward by a distance equal to the pitch.   ☐

c Because the pitch is small the screw moves forward with a small force.   ☐

d With the help of a screw it is possible to lift a car with one hand.   ☐

Gears

1. **Choose the correct words from the brackets to fill the gaps.**

   a A gear is a wheel with _____ around its edge. (threads, cranks, teeth)

   b The teeth on one gear wheel _____ with the teeth on its neighbour (clash, mesh, mash)

   c Two gear wheels with meshed teeth turn in the _____ direction (same, opposite, corresponding).

   d Gears transfer _____ and force from one place to another. (oscillation, translation, rotation)

2. **Which way will the follower gear turn? Draw an arrow.**

   a How many teeth does the driver have?

   _____

   b How many teeth does the follower have?

   _____

   c How many turns will the follower make for each turn of the diver? _____

   d Which gear turns faster? _____

   e Which gear turns with more force? _____

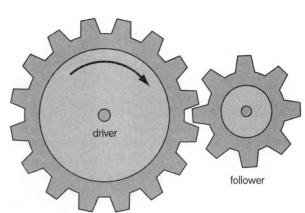

3. **Make some model gears. Photocopy the gears on this page. Stick the copies to card and cut out the gears. Make holes in the centres and fasten the gears to card with paper fasteners. Make sure the gears mesh.**

   Experiment to see how one gear turns another.

Using machines

1. **Name some tools and machines you could use for the tasks in the table. Name both hand (muscle powered) tools and machine (engine powered) tools if you can.**

Task	Hand tool	Machine tool
Drilling a hole		
Lifting a load		
Cutting wood		
Digging a trench		
Moving a pile of earth		
Breaking rocks		
Driving a post into the ground		

2. **Choose the correct words from the brackets to fill the gaps.**

   a Levers, pulleys and wheels are examples of _____ machines. (old, simple, complex)

   b A _____ machine is built from two or more simple machines. (complex, large, modern)

   c A bicycle is an example of a _____ machine. (simple, basic, complex)

   d Many of the modern machines we use in the home are powered by _____. (electricity, steam, water)

3. **Label the parts of this complex machine with the words below.**

   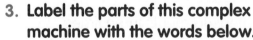

wheel	lever
pulleys	winch

   a_____   b_____

   c_____

   d_____

4. **Tick (✔) the simple machines that you can find as part of a bicycle, put a cross by those you cannot (✗). Discuss your answers as a class. Do you all agree?**

   wheel   lever   pulley   gear

   screw   crank   axle   inclined plane

Investigating friction

1. **Read about this investigation then answer the questions.**

Richard and Ali are investigating the friction between a shoe and different surfaces.

They lay the surface to be tested on a plank and fix it in place.

They stand a shoe on the surface.

They raise one end of the plank slowly until the shoe just starts to slip down the surface.

They measure the angle the plank makes with the floor using a protractor, and record the reading.

They repeat each measurement three times.

Results

Surface	Result 1	Result 2	Result 3	Average
carpet	35°	37°	36°	
linoleum	23°	25°	21°	
wood	31°	27°	29°	
rubber	42°	42°	40°	

a What is the angle of the plank in the diagram? _____

b Explain why Richard and Ali repeated each of their measurements three times.

_____

_____

c Calculate the average slip angle for each surface. Write the averages in the table.

d What conclusions can you form from the results?

_____

_____

Using friction

1. **Give *two* examples of situations where friction is useful.**

   a _____

   b _____

2. **Give *two* examples of situations where friction is wasteful.**

   a _____

   b _____

3. **Match the words to the definitions. Write in the spaces given.**

   (skidding   wear   lubricant   aquaplane   tread)

   a To skid or slide on the surface of water. _____

   b The grooves in a tyre or the sole of a shoe. _____

   c When a vehicle's wheels lose grip and spin or slide on the road. _____

   d Damage caused by friction. _____

   e A substance such as oil that reduces the friction between two surfaces. _____

4. **Investigating friction**

   Investigate the friction between a model car and different surfaces.

   You will need: a toy car, a ramp, a brick or books to raise one end of ramp, a tape measure.

   Instructions:
   - Let the car roll down an inclined plane on to the surface to be tested.
   - Use a tape measure to measure how far the car travels before coming to rest.
   - Record your results in a suitable table.

   Explain how you can make your tests fair and accurate.

   _____

   _____

   _____

   What conclusions can you form?

   _____

   _____

   _____

Light and seeing

1. **Mark each of these statements as true (✔) or false (✗).**

   a The sun is a light source. ☐

   b Light travels in circles. ☐

   c Alexander Graham Bell invented the electric bulb. ☐

   d When you read a book the book is reflecting light into your eyes. ☐

2. **Tick (✔) the torches whose light will reach the eye in the centre of this diagram. Put a cross (✗) by any torch where the light will not reach the eye. (Hint: use a ruler to check.)**

3. **Find the ten light sources in this word square.**

f	l	a	m	e	r	u	n
i	a	b	u	l	b	l	e
r	s	t	a	r	s	e	t
e	e	o	r	t	u	r	f
w	r	r	e	o	n	e	d
o	v	c	a	n	d	l	e
r	i	h	i	y	h	a	t
k	k	h	i	m	f	m	o
m	a	t	c	h	r	p	s

4. **Draw arrows to show how the boy uses light from the lamp to see the book.**

Light and materials

1. **Match these words to their definitions. Write the words in the correct spaces.**

transparent   translucent   opaque   disperse

a Describes a material that light does not pass through. _____

b Describes a material that allows light to pass through, but scatters the light in random directions. _____

c To separate a mixture of different light colours into a spectrum. _____

d Describes a material that allows light to pass straight through it. _____

2. **Write the names of these materials in the correct columns of the table.**

window   glass   metal   milk   tissue paper   black cloth   pure water   rock   air

Transparent	Translucent	Opaque

Add more materials to your table.

3. **Mark each of these statements as true (✔) or false (✗).**

a A mirror absorbs light. ☐

b Shiny metal reflects light. ☐

c You cannot see through a black card because it disperses light. ☐

d When white light is dispersed, it is separated into the colours of the rainbow. ☐

4. **How does light travel?**

 You will need: a bright torch, several sheets of different types of paper.
Instructions:

• Use a bright torch to compare how well different types of paper block light.

• Place a sheet of paper in front of the torch. Can you see the light?

• How many sheets of the paper are needed to block the light completely?

• Record your results in a table.

Type of paper	Number of sheets to block light
photocopy paper	
tissue paper	
drawing paper	

Making shadows

1. **Match these words to their definitions. Write the words in the correct spaces.**

    | shadow   umbra   rays   penumbra |

    a Straight arrows showing the direction in which light is travelling. _____

    b The dark region behind an object from which the object blocks light. _____

    c The outer, partial shadow from which light is only partly blocked. _____

    d The inner, total shadow region from which light is completely blocked by an opaque object. _____

2. **Label this diagram. Use the words in the box.**

    | light source   umbra   penumbra   rays   object |

    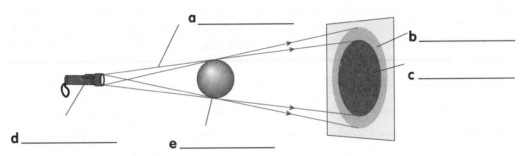

3. **Draw the shadows of these sticks on the ground.**

    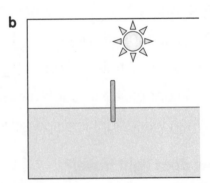

4. **Investigating shadows**

    You will need: a ball like a tennis ball, a torch, a screen.

    Instructions:

    - Predict which ball will cast a larger shadow on the screen.
    - Perform an experiment to test your prediction.

    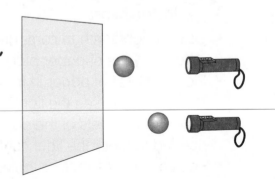

Reflection

1. **Mark each of these statements as true (✔) or false (✘).**

   a The image in a plane (flat) mirror is upside down. ☐

   b The image in a plane mirror is back-to-front. ☐

   c The angle at which a mirror reflects light is equal to the angle at which the light is incident on the mirror. ☐

   d The image in a curved mirror is always smaller than the object. ☐

2. **Write these letters as they would appear in a plane mirror.**

   A   B   L   H   R   P   D   N   F   S

   ___ ___ ___ ___ ___ ___ ___ ___ ___ ___

3. **Draw the light rays reflected by these mirrors.**

   a    b    c

4. **Investigate how the number of images you see in two mirrors depends on the angle between them.**

   Stand two small mirrors at right angles to each other. Stand a small object between them. How many images can you count?

   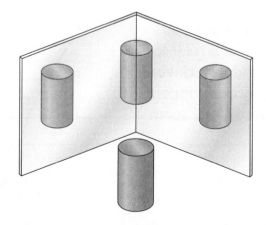

   Change the angle between the mirrors. Describe what you see.

Refraction

1. **Choose the correct words from the brackets to fill the gaps.**

   a When light travels at an angle from one transparent material to another it may change _____. (colour, direction, temperature)

   b This is because light travels at different _____ through different materials. (times, speeds, levels)

   c The direction change described is called _____. (reflection, deflection, refraction)

2. **Name two natural observations that are caused by refraction. (Hint: one gives rise to illusions in the desert, another is very colourful).**

   _____

   _____

3. **Draw the refracted light ray in the glass.**

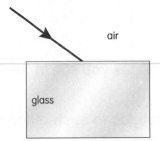

air

glass

4. **Where does the coin appear when you look down into the water? Use a ruler to trace the refracted rays 1 and 2 backwards to the point from which they both appear to come. This is where the coin will seem to be.**

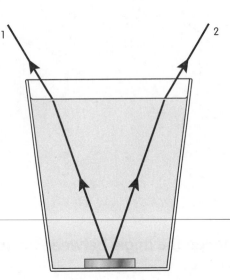

1   2

The eye

1. **Match the words to their definitions. Write the words in the correct spaces.**

pupil   iris   cornea   lens   retina   optic nerve

a The light-sensitive layer that covers the inside surface of the back of the eye.
_____

b The black aperture (hole) at the centre of the iris through which light passes into the eye. _____

c The nerve that carries information from the eye to the brain. _____

d The transparent disc that changes thickness to focus on objects at different distances.
_____

e The coloured ring that surrounds the pupil. _____

f The outer surface of the eye. _____

2. **Mark each of these statements as true (✔) or false (✗).**

a Information from the eye travels as electrical pulses to the brain. ☐

b The lens focuses an image on to the cornea. ☐

c The image produced by the lens is upside down. ☐

d The point closest to the eye at which you can see clearly is called the far point. ☐

3. **On these diagrams of the eye draw the pupils as they would appear in:**

a Bright light   **b** Dim light

4. **Explain briefly the differences between your drawings for Activity 3.**

a In bright light the pupil _____.

b In dim light the pupil _____.

Investigating lenses

1. **Identify these lenses as *concave* or *convex*.**

   a _____   b _____

2. **Draw the light rays after they have passed through the lenses.**

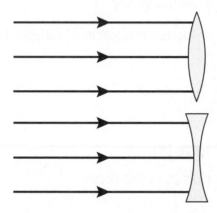

3. **Name the type of lens that concentrates light.** _____

   Name the type of lens that spreads light out. _____

4. **Match these words to their descriptions.**

   ┌─────────────────────────────────────┐
   │ short-sighted   long-sighted   │
   └─────────────────────────────────────┘

   a Describes a person whose eyes concentrate light from distant objects too much
      so that the image is formed in front of the retina. Distant objects are not in focus.

      _____

   b Describes a person whose eyes can concentrate light from near-by objects enough to
      form an image on the retina. Nearby objects are not in focus. _____

5. **Mark each of these statements as true (✔) or false (✗).**

   a A short-sighted person should wear spectacles with concave lenses. ☐

   b A long-sighted person should wear spectacles with convex lenses. ☐

   c A concave lens works as a magnifying glass. ☐

   d A thin convex lens concentrates light more strongly than a thicker lens. ☐

Optical instruments

1. **Find eight optical instruments in this grid.**

z	m	i	c	r	o	s	c	o	p	e
b	a	t	e	l	e	s	c	o	p	e
i	g	p	a	z	y	x	i	g	r	h
n	n	e	j	a	r	b	w	v	o	a
o	i	r	t	k	s	w	m	n	j	p
c	f	i	y	z	l	p	v	t	e	q
u	i	s	a	x	o	w	u	h	c	i
l	e	c	a	m	e	r	a	b	t	c
a	r	o	d	n	m	f	g	k	o	r
r	s	p	c	d	e	l	f	s	r	j
s	p	e	c	t	a	c	l	e	s	t

2. **Mark each of these statements as true (✔) or false (✗).**

   a A pinhole camera uses a lens to focus light. ☐

   b Ibn al-Haythamin invented the pinhole camera a thousand years ago. ☐

   c The image made by a pin-hole camera is upside down. ☐

   d The image in a camera with a lens is the right way up. ☐

3. **How does this pinhole camera form an image of the tree on its screen? Use a ruler to draw light rays from the top and bottom of the tree through the pinhole to the screen. Sketch the image as it will appear.**

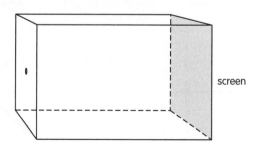

screen

4. **Find out more about the work of Ibn al-Haytham.**

Colour

1. **Match the words to their definitions. Write the words in the correct spaces.**

    > spectrum   filter   absorb   transmit

    a   A band of different colours produced when a mixture of different light colours is dispersed (separated). _____

    b   To allow light (or something else) to pass through. _____

    c   A transparent sheet or disc that only transmits light of a certain colour.

    _____

    d   To soak up or take in something — the energy of light for example. _____

2. **Mark each of these statements as true (✔) or false (✗).**

    a   A blue flower reflects blue light. ☐

    b   A blue flower absorbs red light. ☐

    c   A red filter absorbs red light. ☐

    d   A red filter transmits blue light. ☐

3. **Colour or label these flowers to show how they appear in different colour light.**

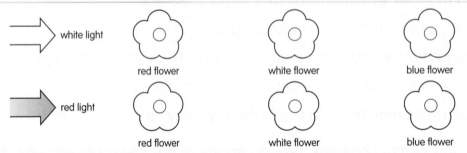

4. **Match each word to the diagram that illustrates it. Draw lines.**

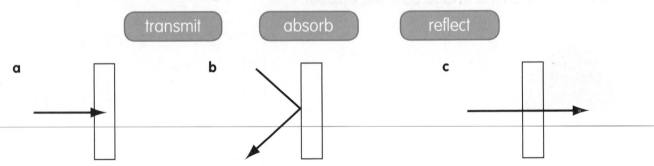

Static electricity

1. **Mark each of these statements as true (✔) or false (✗).**

   a There are two kinds of electric charge. ☐

   b A positive charge repels a negative charge. ☐

   c A negative charge attracts a positive charge. ☐

   d A charged object repels an uncharged object. ☐

2. **Write the missing word for each of these laws of electric charge.**

   a like charges _____

   b unlike charges _____

3. **Richard rubs a plastic rod with a woollen cloth. The cloth and the rod gain equal but opposite electric charges. Label the diagram with words, arrows and charges to show how friction causes charging.**

   friction

4. **Answer the questions.**

   a Describe *two* things you can do to protect yourself in a thunderstorm.

   _____

   _____

   b Describe *two* things you should *not* do in a thunderstorm.

   _____

   _____

Lesson 21

Electric circuits

1. **Write the name of the component under each symbol. Use the words in the box.**

   cell   wire   battery   motor   bulb   switch   buzzer

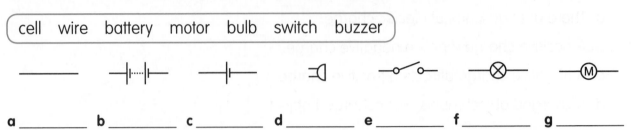

   a _____   b _____   c _____   d _____   e _____   f _____   g _____

2. **Tick (✔) any bulb that lights. Put a cross (✗) by any bulb that does not light.**

   a    b 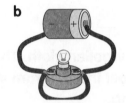   c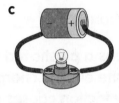

   Explain briefly why the two lamps you have marked with crosses do not light.

   _____

   _____

3. **Draw a circuit to show how you would connect a battery and switch to a lamp, so that the lamp can be switched on and off.**

4. **Which switches must you close to light the lamp? Tick (✔) the correct answer. Put a cross (✗) by the answers which are not correct.**

   a A only
   b B only
   c A and B
   d A and C

   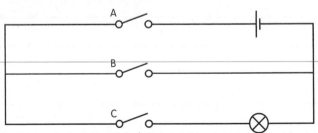

Circuit projects

Activities 1–3 refer to the three circuit projects shown in the diagrams.

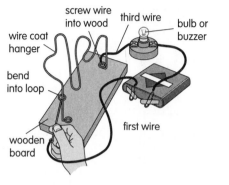

steady hand game

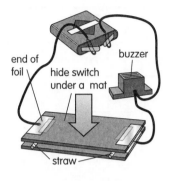

burglar alarm

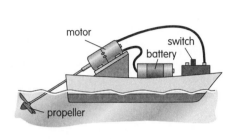

electric boat

1. **Answer the questions.**

   a Which circuit transforms electrical energy into movement energy? _____

   b Which circuit transforms electrical energy into sound energy? _____

   c Which circuit transforms electrical energy into light energy? _____

2. **Draw a circuit diagram for each circuit.**

   a burglar alarm   **b** steady hand game   **c** electric boat

3. **Mark these statements as true (✔) or false (✗).**

   a In the steady hand game the light goes out when the wires touch. ☐

   b The buzzer in the burglar alarm sounds when the circuit is complete. ☐

   c When a burglar steps on the switch in the burglar alarm, he opens a gap in the circuit. ☐

   d If the wires to the battery are connected the other way around (positive and negative are exchanged) the boat travels backwards. ☐

Lesson 23

Magnetic materials

1. Find the ten materials in this word square.

a	l	u	m	i	n	i	u	m
r	n	l	m	r	k	s	p	e
u	i	t	c	o	b	a	l	t
b	c	r	n	n	g	e	a	a
b	k	a	g	l	a	s	s	t
e	e	s	r	p	n	t	t	a
r	l	o	p	p	i	e	i	r
l	o	w	o	o	d	e	c	s
c	o	p	p	e	r	l	e	a

Complete the table using these materials and any others you know.

magnetic materials	non-magnetic materials

2. Read about the experiment described below.
Answer the questions.

Richard and Ali have devised a simple way to compare the strength of magnets.

They tie an iron key to a length of elastic. They tie the other end of the elastic to a table leg. They place the magnet to be tested in contact with the key.

They stretch the elastic slowly by pulling with the magnet. They measure how far the elastic extends before it pulls the key from the magnet.

They repeat each measurement three times for the three magnets.

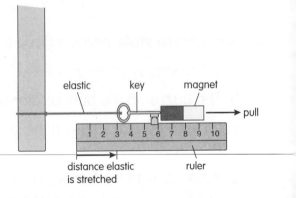

Here are their results:

Distance elastic extends in centimetres				
Magnet	Test 1	Test 2	Test 3	Average
A	10	8	12	
B	23	23	20	
C	14	16	15	

a Explain why Richard and Ali repeated their measurements.

_____

_____

b Calculate the average extension produced by each magnet.

_____

_____

c What conclusions can you form about the relative strengths of the magnets?

_____

_____

3. **Mark these statements as true (✔) or false (✗).**

a All metals are magnetic. ☐

b Iron and steel are magnetic materials. ☐

c Aluminium is a magnetic material. ☐

d Glass, wood and most non-metals are not magnetic materials. ☐

Magnetic poles

1. **Mark each of these statements as true (✔) or false (✗).**

   a Every magnet has two poles. ☐

   b The magnetic force is weakest at the poles. ☐

   c A north pole repels a south pole. ☐

   d A south pole attracts a north pole. ☐

2. **Complete the laws of magnetic force with the missing words.**

   a Like poles _____ .

   b Unlike poles _____ .

3. **Draw arrows to show the forces that act between the magnets in each of these pairs.**

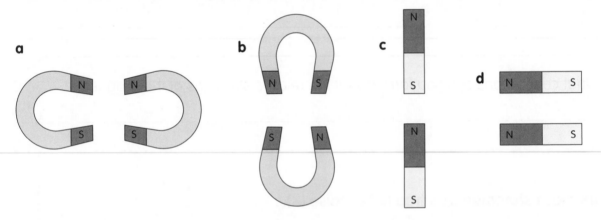

4. **Match the labels to the correct points on the diagram of the Earth. Draw lines.**

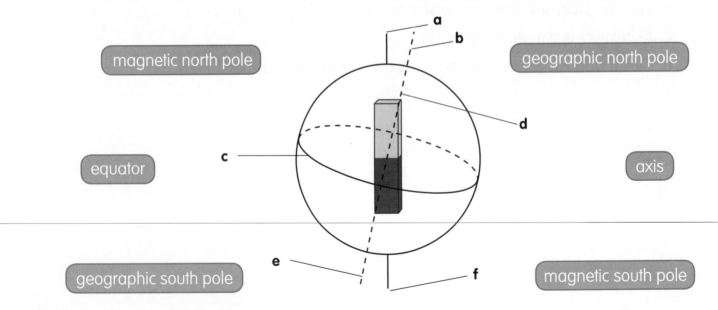

magnetic north pole

geographic north pole

equator

axis

geographic south pole

magnetic south pole

Using magnets

1. Find the ten machines and processes that use magnetism in this word square.

l	o	u	d	s	p	e	a	k	e	r
m	i	c	r	o	p	h	o	n	e	g
o	n	o	o	r	p	o	d	l	y	e
t	o	m	m	w	h	m	m	p	r	n
o	n	p	i	c	k	-	u	p	i	e
r	o	a	s	n	b	y	b	l	l	r
t	o	s	u	r	g	e	r	y	i	a
u	n	s	o	r	t	i	n	g	o	t
r	e	c	o	r	d	i	n	g	r	o
d	o	o	r	-	c	a	t	c	h	r

2. Mark each of these statements as true (✔) or false (✗).

a A computer disc uses magnetism to store information. ☐

b The generator was the first practical application of magnetism. ☐

c An electromagnet can be switched on and off. ☐

d It is better to use a permanent magnet than an electromagnet to lift metal scrap. ☐

3. Answer the questions.

a What is lodestone?

_____

b Why is lodestone important in the history of magnetism?

_____

_____

4. Make a list of magnets around your home. Complete the table to show the different ways in which you make use of magnetism.

Where I found magnets in my home	Uses of magnetism in my home

End-of-unit test 4

Part A

Mark each of these statements as true (✔) or false (✗).

1. Friction speeds things up. ☐

2. Friction acts in the opposite direction to motion. ☐

3. A lubricant increases friction. ☐

4. A concave lens is thicker in the middle than at the edge. ☐

5. A convex lens spreads light out. ☐

6. Short sight can be corrected with concave lenses. ☐

7. When you push against a brick wall you are doing work. ☐

8. Like charges attract. ☐

9. A lever can increase the strength of a force. ☐

10. A prism separates white light into a spectrum. ☐

Part B

Choose the correct word or words to match the description.

1. (opaque translucent transparent reflective)

   A substance that allows rays of light to pass straight through.

2. (penumbra umbra eclipse image)

   The region of a shadow from which only part of the light from the source is blocked.

3. (the electric motor the fridge magnet the magnetic compass the loudspeaker)

   The first practical use of magnetism.

Part C

Select the one correct answer for each question.

1. The diagram shows a moving ball. Which force would you use to slow the ball down?

   a →

   b ←

   c ↑

   d ↓

   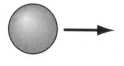

2. Which one of the following is not a force?

   a friction

   b air

   c gravity

   d magnetism

3. The diagram shows a simple machine. What type of machine is it?

   a pulley

   b gear

   c lever

   d wedge

   Crowbar

   effort

   load

4. A screw is a simple machine.
   When you turn the screw it moves forward:

   a with a smaller force

   b with the same force

   c by a greater distance

   d with a greater force

5. Which of the following is a complex machine?

   a axe

   b nutcrackers

   c rowing boat

   d bicycle

6. Which lever could you use to lift the biggest load?

   a   b   c   d

7. Look at the diagram of the eye. The part labelled Z is the:

    a   cornea

    b   retina

    c   lens

    d   iris

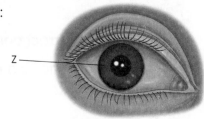

8. Which of these descriptions of a mirror image is not true?

    a   It is back-to-front.

    b   It looks as if it is behind the mirror but it is not really there.

    c   It is caused by light bouncing from the surface of the mirror.

    d   It is upside down.

9. Two positively charged rods are held next to each other as shown in the diagram. Which of the following will occur when they are released?

    a   They will move away from each other.

    b   They will move towards each other.

    c   They will remain in the same position.

    d   A spark will jump from one rod to the other.

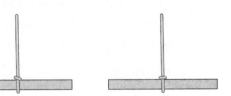

10. During a thunderstorm all of the following are advisable except:

    a   sheltering in a building or enclosed vehicle

    b   carrying an umbrella

    c   lying flat on the ground if caught in an open flat place

    d   avoiding tall trees and other isolated objects

11. Which item will not be attracted by a magnet?

    a   an iron nail

    b   a steel can

    c   an aluminium can

    d   a wire paper clip

Part D

Match each item in column A to the correct definition in column B.

A	B
1. retina	**a** The coloured ring that surrounds the pupil in the eye.
2. cornea	**b** The light-sensitive layer that covers the inside surface of the back of the eye.
3. pupil	**c** The transparent disc in the eye that changes shape to focus on objects at different distances.
4. iris	**d** The strong transparent protective covering that forms the outer surface of the eye.
	e The black aperture (space) through which light passes into the eye.

Part E

Explain in a few sentences:

1. How you can use a lever to lift a heavy load more easily

2. How you can show that light travels in straight lines

3. Why the water in a swimming pool looks shallower than it really is

4. Why when you rub a toy balloon with a cloth, it attracts scraps of paper

5. How a switch turns an electric circuit off and on

Day, night and the seasons

1. **Use the words below to label this diagram.**

   sun   Earth   day   night   Earth's axis

2. **Mark each of these statements as true (✔) or false (✘).**

   a The Earth takes one day to make one orbit of the sun. ☐

   b The Earth spins on its axis once each day. ☐

   c One year is the time the Earth takes to make one orbit of the sun. ☐

   d In December it is winter in the southern hemisphere. ☐

3. **Look at these diagrams of the Earth in its orbit around the sun.**

   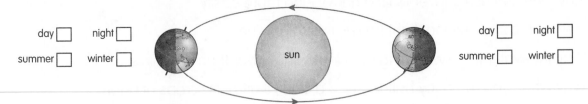

   day ☐   night ☐   sun   day ☐   night ☐
   summer ☐   winter ☐   summer ☐   winter ☐

   On each diagram of the Earth:

   a Mark the position of your home on the Earth.

   b Tick the box to say if it is day or night at your home.

   c Tick the box to say if it is summer or winter.

   Explain your answers.

   _____

   _____

4. **Match each statement to its explanation. Draw lines.**

   We have day and night because

   a countries near the equator face the sun more directly.

   We have seasons because

   b the Earth spins on its axis.

   Egypt is hotter than England because

   c the Earth's axis is tilted to its orbit.

The phases of the moon

1. **Match these descriptions of the moon to the pictures. Draw lines.**

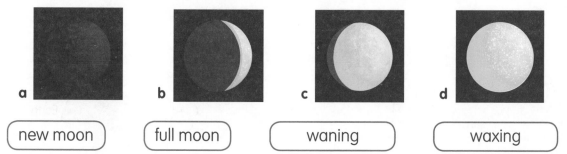

a   b   c   d

(new moon)   (full moon)   (waning)   (waxing)

2. **Mark each of these statements as true (✔) or false (✗).**

   a A new moon is very bright. ☐

   b The moon takes just over 27 days to orbit the Earth. ☐

   c The moon is a hot ball of gas. ☐

   d The moon is a cold ball of rock. ☐

3. **This sequence shows the phases of the moon from one new moon to the next. Answer the questions.**

   a On which day is the moon full: day 1, day 15 or day 28? _____

   b On which days is the moon waxing: days 1-14 or days 15-30? _____

   c List the days on which the moon is waning.

   _____

4. **Look at this diagram of the sun, the Earth and the moon. The moon is shown in three different places in its orbit, X, Y and Z.**

a Shade the dark sides of the moon and Earth that face away from the sun.

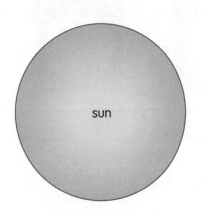

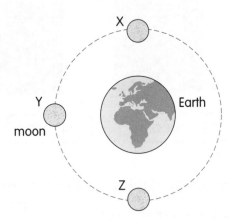

b Draw the moon as it would appear to observers on Earth when it is at each of the positions X, Y and Z.

Eclipses of the sun and the moon

1. Shade / colour these outlines of the sun to show its appearance:

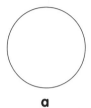
a

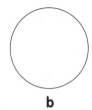
b

a During a total eclipse.

b During a partial eclipse.

2. Match these words to their definitions. Write the words in the correct spaces below.

solar eclipse   lunar eclipse   total eclipse   partial eclipse

a When an observer stands in the umbra of the moon's shadow on Earth and observes the moon covering the whole sun. _____

b Observed when the Earth passes between the sun and the moon and the Earth's shadow falls on the moon. _____

c Observed when the moon passes between the sun and the Earth and the moon's shadow falls on the Earth. _____

d When an observer stands in the penumbra of the moon's shadow on Earth and observes the moon partly covering the sun. _____

3. Draw the arrangement of the sun, moon and Earth during a solar eclipse.

4. Draw the arrangement of the sun, moon and Earth during a lunar eclipse.

End-of-unit test 5

Part A

Mark each of these statements as true (✔) or false (✗).

1. The sun travels around the Earth. ☐
2. The Earth spins once a day. ☐
3. We have seasons because the Earth's axis is tilted. ☐
4. In June the southern hemisphere is tilted towards the sun. ☐
5. The moon travels around the Earth. ☐
6. We see the part of the moon that faces away from the sun. ☐
7. A new moon is very bright. ☐
8. In a solar eclipse the moon's shadow falls on the Earth. ☐
9. In a lunar eclipse the Earth's shadow falls on the sun. ☐
10. The sun and the moon look almost the same size in the sky. ☐
11. The moon is much bigger that the sun. ☐

Part B

Choose the correct word or words to match the description.

1. (partial eclipse   total eclipse   solar eclipse   lunar eclipse)

   When the Earth passes between the sun and the moon and the Earth's shadow falls on the moon.

2. (equator   orbit   axis   umbra)

   The line between the North Pole and the South Pole around which the Earth spins.

3. (new moon   full moon   waxing   waning)

   The change in brightness of the moon when it is getting brighter from one day to the next.

Part C

Select the one correct answer for each question.

1. Complete this sentence. The sun rises and sets each day because:
   a the Earth is spinning
   b the sun is spinning
   c the sun is orbiting the Earth
   d the sun is moving through the atmosphere

2. Which of the following best describes the sun?
   a a sphere of rock and metal
   b a planet
   c a sphere of hot burning gas
   d a fiery disc

3. Complete this sentence. It is day on the side of the Earth that is:
   a turned away from the sun
   b in the sun's shadow
   c furthest from the sun
   d facing the sun

4. When is the moon brightest? When it is...
   a new
   b waning
   c full
   d waxing

5. What is the arrangement of the sun, Earth and moon during a solar eclipse?
   a sun-Earth-moon
   b Earth-sun-moon
   c Earth-moon-sun
   d moon-Earth-sun

6. Which one of these statements is true?
   a There is a solar eclipse once each month.
   b Solar eclipses occur when the moon is full.
   c A solar eclipse is seen when the moon's shadow falls on the Earth.
   d Everyone on the daylight side of the Earth can see a total eclipse at the same time.

7. One year is the time for:
    a The moon to complete one orbit of the Earth
    b The Earth to spin once on its axis
    c The Earth to complete one orbit of the sun
    d The sun to complete one orbit of the Earth

Part D

Match each item in column A to the correct definition in column B.

A
1. eclipse
2. seasons
3. orbit
4. phases of the moon

B
a The path a planet, moon or other satellite follows around a more massive object in space.
b The total shadow region from which light is completely blocked by an opaque object.
c When light from an object in space is blocked by another object passing in front of it.
d Times of the year with particular weather conditions (winter and summer).
e The changes in the shape of the moon we observe through the month.

Part E

Explain in a few sentences:

1. Why we have day and night
2. Why summer is hotter than winter
3. Why we can see the moon when it does not give out light itself
4. Why a new moon is dark and a full moon is bright
5. The differences between a solar eclipse and a lunar eclipse

Macmillan Education
Between Towns Road, Oxford OX4 3PP
A division of Macmillan Publishers Limited
Companies and representatives throughout the world

ISBN: 978-0-230-02855-5

Design by Clare Webber
Typeset by 🗲 Tek-Art, Crawley Down, West Sussex
Illustrated by 🗲 Tek-Art
Cover design by Bigtop Design Limited
Cover photographs by **Corbis**/A. Bannister/Gallo Images (crystal),
Getty Images/Photodisc (mercury).

The authors and publisher would like to thank the following for
permission to reproduce their photographs:
Macmillan/ Brand X p4–p19 (unit 1 icon), Macmillan New Zealand
p20–p34 (unit 2 icon), Macmillan/ Getty p35–p56 (unit 3 icon),
Macmillan/ Getty p57–p87 (unit 4 icon), Macmillan/ Photodisc
p88–p94 (unit 5 icon).

Printed in Malaysia

2016 2015 2014 2013
10 9 8 7 6 5 4 3